PRENTICE HALL

# UNITED STATES HISTORY

*CURRICULUM*

# All-in-One
# Teaching Resources

---

## The Coming of War
## (1931–1942)

PEARSON

Prentice
Hall

Upper Saddle River, New Jersey
Boston, Massachusetts

PEARSON
Prentice
Hall

Upper Saddle River, New Jersey
Boston, Massachusetts

ISBN 0-13-203687-8

1 2 3 4 5 6 7 8 9 10   10 09 08 07 06

## THE COMING OF WAR

# Letter Home

Dear Family,

Over the coming weeks, our United States history class will be reading a chapter called The Coming of War. The following information will give you some background to the content your student will be studying.

Following the end of World War I, Germany had been forced to pay reparations to the Allies for the losses suffered during the war. Although peace had been reached, it was a tentative peace. The rise of the Nazi party in Germany, led by Adolf Hitler, brought about a new militarism, despite restrictions on rebuilding its military after World War I. Both Germany and Italy sought to expand their power by invading other countries during the 1930s. In Asia, Japan expanded its empire by invading neighboring Manchuria in 1931. By the end of the 1930s, it seemed clear that war would break out again in Europe and in Asia.

After the losses of World War I, the United States was reluctant to enter another European war. However, Roosevelt openly opposed the aggression of Germany and Japan, which put him at odds with those countries and opened the United States to attacks. As Germany unleashed its attacks on Europe, the United States remained neutral, watching as most of the continent fell to the German army. By 1940, Germany controlled the European mainland and sought to defeat Great Britain. The British were able to defend their country with their air force. Although the United States supported the Allies during this period, there was considerable debate as to whether the country should enter the war. It was not until the United States was attacked at Pearl Harbor on December 7, 1941, that the United States entered World War II. Although the United States was able to mobilize quickly for the war, many difficult battles in the Pacific during 1942 proved that this war would not be easily won.

In the weeks ahead, your student may wish to share what he or she is learning with you. Please participate in your child's educational experience through discussion and involvement.

Sincerely,

# Carta para el hogar

Estimada familia,

En las próximas semanas, nuestra clase de historia de Estados Unidos va a leer un capítulo llamado "La llegada de la guerra". La siguiente información le dará a usted algunos conocimientos sobre el tema que su estudiante va a estudiar.

Luego de la Primera Guerra Mundial, Alemania fue forzada a pagar reparaciones a los Aliados por las pérdidas ocasionadas durante la guerra. Aunque se había logrado la paz, ésta era sólo tentativa. El surgimiento de partido Nazi en Alemania, liderado por Adolf Hitler, trajo consigo un nuevo militarismo, a pesar de las restricciones para reconstruir sus fuerzas armadas luego de la Primera Guerra Mundial. Tanto Alemania como Italia buscaron expandir su control invadiendo otros países durante la década de 1930. En Asia, Japón expandió su imperio invadiendo el vecino Manchuria en 1931. A finales de la década de 1930, la guerra era inminente nuevamente en Europa y Asia.

Luego de las pérdidas de la Primera Guerra Mundial, Estados Unidos no quería participar en otra guerra en Europa. Sin embargo, Roosevelt se opuso abiertamente a la agresión por parte de Alemania y Japón, lo cual lo puso en contra de esos países y expuso a Estados Unidos a ataques. A medida que Alemania castigaba con sus ataques a Europa, Estados Unidos se mantenía neutral, mirando como la mayor parte del continente caía ante el ejército alemán. Para 1940, Alemania controlaba el continente europeo y buscaba derrotar a Gran Bretaña. Los británicos fueron capaces de defender su país con su fuerza aérea. Aunque Estados Unidos apoyaba a los aliados durante este período, había un gran debate acerca de la participación del país en la guerra. No fue sino hasta que Estados Unidos fue atacado en Pearl Harbor el 7 de diciembre de 1941, que el país ingresó a la Segunda Guerra Mundial. Aunque Estados Unidos pudo movilizarse rápidamente para la guerra, muchas batallas difíciles en el Pacífico durante 1942 probaron que esta guerra no se ganaría fácilmente.

En las próximas semanas, es posible que su estudiante quiera compartir con usted lo que ha aprendido. Por favor participe en la experiencia educativa de su hijo o hija a través de conversaciones e involucrándose en su trabajo.

Atentamente,

**THE COMING OF WAR 1931–1942**

# 1. Dictators and War

*Pacing*
2 periods
1 block

L1 Special Needs
L2 Basic to Average
L3 All Students
L4 Average to Advanced

## Section Objectives

■ Explain how dictators and militarist regimes arose in several countries in the 1930s.

■ Summarize the actions taken by aggressive regimes in Europe and Asia.

■ Analyze the responses of Britain, France, and the United States to the aggressive regimes.

**Terms and People** • totalitarianism • Joseph Stalin • Benito Mussolini • Adolf Hitler • antisemitic • Spanish Civil War • appeasement • Anschluss • Munich Pact

**Focus Question:** Why did aggressive totalitarian states rise after World War I, and what did they do?

### PREPARE TO READ

**Build Background Knowledge**
Preview the section and remind students that the United States did not join the League of Nations.

**Set a Purpose**
Have students discuss the Witness History Selection. Point out the Section Focus Question and have students fill in the Note Taking graphic organizer.

**Preview Key Terms**
Preview the section's Key Terms.

**Instructional Resources**
❏ **WITNESS HISTORY** Audio CD
❏ **All in One Teaching Resources**
   L3 Preread the Chapter, p. 7
   L3 Analyze Visuals, p. 9
   L3 Vocabulary Builder, p. 10
   L3 Reading Strategy, p. 11
❏ **Reading and Note Taking Study Guide**
   (On-Level, Adapted, and Spanish)
   Section 1

### TEACH

**A Bitter Peace Unravels**
Explore problems caused by the Versailles Treaty.

**Repression in the Soviet Union and Italy**
Understand the growth of totalitarian governments in the Soviet Union and Italy.

**Aggressive Leaders in Germany and Japan**
Analyze the rise of power of Adolf Hitler in Germany and militarists in Japan.

**Dictators Turn to Aggression**
Discuss acts of aggression by European dictators in the 1930s.

**Aggression Goes Unchecked**
Explain the policy of appeasement, and how it failed to prevent further military action.

**Instructional Resources**
❏ **All in One Teaching Resources**
   L3 Outline Map: German Aggression, p. 14
❏ **Color Transparencies**
   L3 The Nazi Party
❏ **Note Taking Transparencies,** B-111a, B-111b

### ASSESS/RETEACH

**Assess Progress**
Evaluate student comprehension with the Section Assessment and Section Quiz.

**Reteach**
Assign the Reading and Note Taking Study Guide to help struggling students.

**Extend**
Have students debate the policy of appeasement.

**Instructional Resources**
❏ **All in One Teaching Resources**
   L3 Section Quiz, p. 19
❏ **Reading and Note Taking Study Guide**
   Section 1 Summary
❏ **Progress Monitoring Transparencies,** 107

THE COMING OF WAR 1931–1942

# 2. From Isolation to Involvement

*Pacing*
2 periods
1 block

**L1** Special Needs
**L2** Basic to Average
**L3** All Students
**L4** Average to Advanced

## Section Objectives

■ Understand the course of the early years of World War II in Europe.

■ Describe Franklin Roosevelt's foreign policy in the mid-1930s and the great debate between interventionists and isolationists.

■ Explain how the United States became more involved in the conflict.

**Terms and People** • blitzkrieg • Axis Powers • Allies • Winston Churchill • Neutrality Act of 1939 • Tripartite Pact • Lend-Lease Act • Atlantic Charter

**Focus Question:** How did Americans react to events in Europe and Asia in the early years of World War II?

### PREPARE TO READ

**Build Background Knowledge**
Preview the section and ask students to think about why Americans favored isolation.

**Set a Purpose**
Have students discuss the Witness History Selection. Point out the Section Focus Question and have students fill in the Note Taking graphic organizer.

**Preview Key Terms**
Preview the section's Key Terms.

**Instructional Resources**
❏ **WITNESS HISTORY** Audio CD

❏ **All in One Teaching Resources**
❏ **Reading and Note Taking Study Guide**
(On-Level, Adapted, and Spanish)
Section 2

### TEACH

**Roosevelt Opposes Aggression**
Understand reactions to Japan's aggression.

**War Erupts in Europe**
Analyze the impact of the German blitzkrieg.

**Americans Debate Involvement**
Discuss the views of American interventionists and isolationists towards the war.

**America Takes Steps Toward War**
Explain the importance of the Lend-Lease Act.

**Instructional Resources**
❏ **All in One Teaching Resources**
**L3** Interpreting a Political Cartoon: Neutrality, p. 15
**L1 L2** Primary Source: The "Four Freedoms" Speech, p. 16
**L3** Primary Source: The "Four Freedoms" Speech and George W. Bush's Address to a Joint Session of Congress, p. 17
❏ **Skills Handbook**
**L3** Distinguish Between Fact and Opinion/ Recognize Bias, p. 13
❏ **Color Transparencies**
**L3** German Blitzkrieg
❏ **Note Taking Transparencies,** B-112

### ASSESS/RETEACH

**Assess Progress**
Evaluate student comprehension with the Section Assessment and Section Quiz.

**Reteach**
Assign the Reading and Note Taking Study Guide to help struggling students.

**Extend**
Have students dramatize an FDR fireside chat.

**Instructional Resources**
❏ **All in One Teaching Resources**
**L4** Enrichment: Oral History, p. 12
**L3** Section Quiz, p. 20
❏ **Reading and Note Taking Study Guide**
Section 2 Summary
❏ **Progress Monitoring Transparencies,** 108

THE COMING OF WAR 1931–1942

# 3. America Enters the War

*Pacing*
2 periods
1 block

**L1** Special Needs
**L2** Basic to Average
**L3** All Students
**L4** Average to Advanced

## Section Objectives

■ Explain why Japan decided to attack Pearl Harbor, and describe the attack itself.

■ Outline how the United States mobilized for war after the attack on Pearl Harbor.

■ Summarize the course of the war in the Pacific through the summer of 1942.

**Terms and People** • Hideki Tojo • Pearl Harbor • WAC • Douglas MacArthur • Bataan Death March • Battle of Coral Sea

**Focus Question:** How did the United States react to the Japanese attack on Pearl Harbor?

## PREPARE TO READ

### Build Background Knowledge
Preview the section and ask students to think about other events that eventually led to American military action against another nation.

### Set a Purpose
Have students discuss the Witness History Selection. Point out the Section Focus Question and have students fill in the Note Taking graphic organizer.

### Preview Key Terms
Preview the section's Key Terms.

### Instructional Resources
❑ **WITNESS HISTORY** Audio CD
❑ **All in One Teaching Resources**
❑ **Reading and Note Taking Study Guide**
(On-Level, Adapted, and Spanish)
Section 3

## TEACH

### Japan Attacks the United States
Understand the causes and effects of the attack on Pearl Harbor.

### Mobilizing for War
Analyze how Americans and American industry responded after the nation entered World War II.

### Fierce Fighting in the Pacific
Discuss early American defeats and victories in the Pacific.

### Instructional Resources
❑ **All in One Teaching Resources**
**L3** Reading a Chart: Industry During World War II, p. 18
❑ **Color Transparencies**
**L3** Women and the War Effort
❑ **Note Taking Transparencies,** B-113a, B-113b

## ASSESS/RETEACH

### Assess Progress
Evaluate student comprehension with the Section Assessment and Section Quiz.

### Reteach
Assign the Reading and Note Taking Study Guide to help struggling students.

### Extend
Extend the lesson by having students complete the online activity on Pearl Harbor.

### Instructional Resources
❑ **All in One Teaching Resources**
**L3** Section Quiz, p. 21
**L1 L2** Chapter Test A, p. 22
**L3** Chapter Test B, p. 25
❑ **Reading and Note Taking Study Guide**
Section 3 Summary
❑ **Progress Monitoring Transparencies,** 109

## THE COMING OF WAR
# Preread the Chapter: Why and How?

What is **Prereading?** It is a reading comprehension strategy. This graphic organizer aids you in prereading this chapter.

**Checklist:** *Place a check on the line when you have completed the following:*

_____ Read all items in the Chapter Opener.

_____ Read the titles of the charts, graphs, maps, and timeline in the Quick Study Guide and Concept Connector Cumulative Review.

_____ Read the chapter assessment.

Before you read each section of your text, look at the following material. (Chapters may have 3, 4, or 5 sections.) Check the sections as you complete the review.

Sections: 1_____ 2_____ 3_____ 4_____ 5_____ Read the Focus Question, the section opener information in the side column, and each boldface heading and subheading.

Sections: 1_____ 2_____ 3_____ 4_____ 5_____ Looked over all words that are underlined or in boldface type.

Sections: 1_____ 2_____ 3_____ 4_____ 5_____ Read all review questions within the section.

*Complete the following:*

**1.** Chapter title: _____

**2.** Write the main idea of each section based on its Focus Question.

Section 1: _____

_____

Section 2: _____

_____

Section 3: _____

_____

Section 4: _____

_____

Section 5: _____

_____

Name _____ Class _____ Date _____

## Preread the Chapter: Why and How? *(Continued)*

**3.** List three visual aids included in the chapter (e.g., pictures, maps, charts, diagrams, features). Describe how they will aid your understanding of the chapter.

(1) _____

_____

(2) _____

_____

(3) _____

_____

**4.** Describe one new or important idea you learned from reading the Quick Study Guide.

_____

_____

**5.** Identify two unfamiliar words that you noticed during your prereading, and determine from the context what you think the new word means.

Word #1 _____ Part of Speech _____

Clues to meaning _____

Predicted meaning _____

Word #2 _____ Part of Speech _____

Clues to meaning _____

Predicted meaning _____

**6.** After previewing this chapter, were you able to understand what the chapter is about?

Not understood _____ Somewhat understood _____ Easily understood _____

**7.** Copy the heading (titles in blue print) that you predict will be the most difficult to understand.

_____

_____

**8.** How many pages are in the chapter? _____

**9.** Estimate the time it will take you to read the chapter. _____

Name _____ Class _____ Date _____

## Analyze Visuals

Images are an effective way to communicate information. There are many types of visuals, such as photographs, paintings, and Infographics. Visuals tell a story in a dramatic or vivid style. Just as with any primary or secondary source, it is important to look closely and ask questions to determine the meaning and reliability of the visual.

Use this outline to help you better understand ideas or events conveyed by a visual. Answer these questions to the best of your ability.

Title of visual  Page

1. What is the topic of the visual (what is happening)?

   _____

2. Focus on the details and list three that you find in the visual. How does each help convey information about the topic?

   _____

   _____

   _____

3. Assume you are one of the individuals in the picture, or that you were present when the image was made.

   (a) Describe who you are.

   _____

   (b) Explain what your reaction might have been to the situation.

   _____

   _____

4. The creator often reveals a bias about the subject or an attempt to get a response from the viewer. Is there anything you see in the image that tells the creator's point of view?

   _____

   _____

5. Write your own caption for the image.

   _____

**THE COMING OF WAR**

# Vocabulary Builder

## Recognize Related Words

As you read, you will encounter many words that you do not know. However, many of these words may look familiar to you. **Related words** are words that share word parts. Knowing the meaning of a related word can help you figure out the meaning of a new or more difficult word. Learning the meanings of related words also helps you remember and use new vocabulary. The example below lists several related words for *ideology.*

| Example |
|---|
| **ideology** a system of ideas that guides an individual, a movement, or a political program |
| **idea** a thought, an opinion, a belief, a plan, or a conception that one thinks or imagines |
| **ideal** thought of as perfect, or exactly as one would wish |
| **ideogram** a symbol that represents an idea |
| **ideologue** an advocate of a specific way of thinking or a particular belief system |
| **logic** the science of reasoning |
| **logistics** the system for managing the details of an undertaking |

**Directions:** *Write the definition for the words listed below. Then use a dictionary to find and record two related words and their definitions for each word. On a separate sheet of paper, write a sentence for each Vocabulary Builder word and for each related word.*

**1. coordinate**

_____

_____

_____

**2. evaluate**

_____

_____

**3. minimal**

_____

_____

## THE COMING OF WAR

# Reading Strategy

## Summarize

Summarizing helps you identify and remember important information in a paragraph or other text. The first step in summarizing is to identify the main idea of the text. The second step is to write a short statement, or summary, about the main idea.

A summary is always shorter than the original text. This means that to write a summary, you leave out less important details and combine others under a single concept.

Read the following paragraph.

> Adolph Hitler became head of the German government in 1933. Defying the Treaty of Versailles, he rebuilt the country's army, navy, and air force. Wanting to unify all people of Germanic descent into one state, Hitler began using his military might to claim areas outside Germany. In 1935, he reclaimed the Saar region, and in 1936 he challenged the League of Nations by sending troops into the Rhineland.

Now look at the summary below.

> After rising to power in 1933, Hitler rebuilt Germany's military and used these forces to claim more land in defiance of the international community.

The summary leaves out some details and combines others under single concepts. References to Germany's army, navy, and air force are combined under the term "military," references to the Saar region and Rhineland are combined under the term "more land," and references to the Treaty of Versailles and League of Nation are combined under the term "international community."

**Directions:** *Read the text in Section 1 under the subheading "Stalin's Grip on the Soviet Union." On the lines provided, answer the questions below.*

> **Hint:** A summary leaves out some details and combines others under a single concept.

1. Which details do you think you could leave out in a summary of the text?

   _____

   _____

2. Which details do you think you can combine under a single concept? Explain.

   _____

   _____

3. Write a summary of the reading passage on a separate sheet of paper. How long is your summary compared to the reading passage?

   _____

   _____

Name _____ Class _____ Date _____

## Enrichment: Oral History

# FDR's Fireside Chats

President Roosevelt used the radio to keep Americans informed about decisions and policies he made. Instead of making speeches, however, he took an informal approach by speaking as if he were sitting and talking with people in the comfort of their homes. After hearing FDR's radio address about the New Deal on May 7, 1933, a reporter decided to call these radio talks "fireside chats." The term stuck. At least 31 of FDR's radio speeches have been called fireside chats.

**Your assignment:** Work in a group to research Roosevelt's September 3, 1939, fireside chat on the outbreak of World War II. Use the information to plan and present a dramatization of an oral history interview on the following topic: Americans Remember Their Reactions to the Outbreak of World War II.

**Suggested materials:** an image of FDR giving a radio address; audio recording of FDR's September 3, 1939, radio address; an image of a 1930s-style radio; cardboard fireplace; three school chairs covered with throws to create a comfortable look; and an audio or video recorder. For tips on conducting an oral history interview, see Oral History Interview Tips on the next page.

**Suggested procedure:**

1. Use your library or online resources to find the text and an audio recording of FDR's September 3, 1939, fireside chat.

2. Read and listen to the text.

3. Use your textbook, library, or online resources to find examples of how ordinary Americans responded to the outbreak of war.

4. Draft a list of five questions you would like to ask someone who had heard FDR's live broadcast on September 3, 1939. Use the text of FDR's address to help you develop questions. Remember, you are doing only a 15- to 20-minute dramatization, so ask only five questions.

5. To prepare for the dramatization, create and develop three characters: one contemporary teenager who will conduct the interview and two adults in their nineties who will share their reactions to the outbreak of war. Consider giving the two adults different points of view. For example, one character want the United States to enter the war immediately, but the other hopes that the United States will continue to stay neutral.

6. Draft a script that follows an oral history interview format (see oral history interview tips on the next page). Consider beginning your script with a five-minute audio segment of the September 3 broadcast to create an atmosphere for your student audience and to stimulate memories for your adult characters.

## Enrichment: Oral History

### FDR's Fireside Chats

7. After drafting the script, assign roles and practice your parts. Listen as you speak your parts, and be ready to revise the script if something doesn't sound right.

8. Identify props needed to recreate a 1939 setting for presidential fireside chats: a photo of FDR, an image of or replica of a 1930s-style radio, a cardboard fireplace, and comfortable looking chairs.

9. Borrow and learn to use an audio or video recorder for use during the dramatization. Although you will not be conducting a real oral history interview, you will be pretending to do this in the dramatization.

10. Conduct at least one dress rehearsal with all three characters, making sure that you know how to use the audio or video recording equipment and that your five-minute audio segment of FDR is appropriately cued.

**Oral History Interview Tips:**

1. Prepare questions in advance. Questions should be open-ended, which means that they should be stated in a way that encourages more than a "yes" or "no" response. For example, instead of asking, "Did you feel upset when the President announced that Germany had invaded Poland" ask, "Tell me about your initial reactions to the news."

2. Oral interviews follow these steps: (a) the interviewer introduces himself or herself, explains why he or she wants to conduct the interview, and asks permission to use audio or video equipment to tape the interview; (b) the interviewer asks the interviewees to share general information about themselves, for example, their name, birth date, location of birth, and community where they lived; (c) the interviewer asks his or her prepared questions; and (d) the interviewer thanks the participants for their time. (After a real interview, the interviewer would send a thank-you note to the participants.)

3. The interviewer's job is to show genuine interest in the interview participants and their stories and to make them feel comfortable during the process. The interviewer's job is to document what the participants say, not to make judgments about the correctness of the participants' views or the accuracy of their memories.

**Suggested resources:** For photo images of FDR and audio recordings of his fireside chats, use the Internet to research the Franklin D. Roosevelt Presidential Library and Museum. For instructions on how to conduct an oral history interview and/or examples of how ordinary Americans reacted to news of the war, use the web site for the Library of Congress American Memory.

Name _____ Class _____ Date _____

## German Aggression

**Directions:** *Shade the land that Germany claimed in 1935–1938, using a different color to represent each of these years: 1935, 1936, 1938. In the blank box, create a color key for your finished map. You may use any map in the textbook chapter, unit opener, or atlas for reference.*

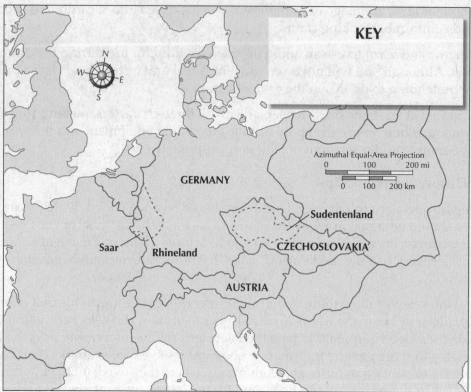

Mapping Specialists Limited

**THE COMING OF WAR**

# Interpreting a Political Cartoon

As Germany and Japan made aggressive advances toward other nations, Americans debated the wisdom of becoming involved in another war. Isolationists advised complete neutrality while Interventionists argued that providing aid to the Allies would keep war from America's shores. Political cartoonists helped bring the debate to life.

◆ *Examine the political cartoon below. Then answer the questions on a separate sheet of paper.*

## Neutrality

*Herb Block's 1935 cartoon "No Foreign Entanglements",* Image courtesy of the
Prints & Photographs Division, Library of Congress, LC-DIG-ppmsc-03382

## Questions to Think About

**1.** What do you think the man standing on American soil represents? Explain.

**2.** Why do you think the man is holding up his hand?

**3.** What do you think all the boats and airplanes represent? Why?

**4.** What do you think the cartoonist was saying about the involvement of the United States in foreign affairs?

**THE COMING OF WAR**

# Primary Source

Franklin Delano Roosevelt used his 1941 State of the Union address to describe four important freedoms. ◆ *As you read an excerpt from his speech, think about the stand he was asking Americans to take.*

## The "Four Freedoms" Speech

| **Summary of Speech** | **Purpose of Speech** |
|---|---|
| What freedoms did Roosevelt say all people have? | Why did Roosevelt think it was important to talk about these freedoms? |

In the future days, which we seek to make secure, we look forward to a world founded upon four essential human freedoms.

The first is freedom of speech and expression—everywhere in the world.

The second is freedom of every person to worship God in his own way—everywhere in the world.

The third is freedom from want—which, translated into world terms, means economic understandings which will secure to every nation a healthy peacetime life for its inhabitants—everywhere in the world.

The fourth is freedom from fear—which, translated into world terms, means a world-wide reduction of armaments to such a point and in such a thorough fashion that no nation will be in a position to commit an act of physical aggression against any neighbor—anywhere in the world. . . .

This nation has placed its destiny in the hands and heads and hearts of its millions of free men and women; and its faith in freedom under the guidance of God. Freedom means the supremacy of human rights every-where. Our support goes to those who struggle to gain those rights or keep them. Our strength is our unity of purpose. To that high concept there can be no end save victory.

—President Franklin D. Roosevelt's State of the Union Address, January 6, 1941

| **Context of Speech** | **Legacy** |
|---|---|
| What world and national events made Roosevelt give this speech? | How well do you think Roosevelt's speech helped Americans understand the war in Europe? |

# Primary Source

On September 20, 2001, after the attacks on America on September 11, President George W. Bush addressed a joint session of Congress to discuss the state of the Union. His speech answered Americans' questions about the terrorist attacks and discussed the freedoms granted to all Americans. ◆ *Read the following excerpts from the Address to a Joint Session of Congress. As you read, compare this address to FDR's "Four Freedoms" speech. Then answer the questions that follow.*

## The "Four Freedoms" Speech and George W. Bush's Address to a Joint Session of Congress

**President George W. Bush's Address to a Joint Session of Congress on the 9/11 Attacks**

Tonight we are a country awakened to danger and called to defend freedom. Our grief has turned to anger, and anger to resolution. Whether we bring our enemies to justice, or bring justice to our enemies, justice will be done.

Americans are asking, why do they hate us? . . . They hate our freedoms—our freedom of religion, our freedom of speech, our freedom to vote and assemble and disagree with each other.

Americans are asking: How will we fight and win this war? We will direct every resource at our command—every means of diplomacy, every tool of intelligence, every instrument of law enforcement, every financial influence,

and every necessary weapon of war—to the disruption and to the defeat of the global terror network.

I ask you to uphold the values of America, and remember why so many have come here. We are in a fight for our principles, and our first responsibility is to live by them. No one should be singled out for unfair treatment or unkind words because of their ethnic background or religious faith.

Great harm has been done to us. We have suffered great loss. . . . We will rally the world to this cause by our efforts, by our courage. We will not tire, we will not falter, and we will not fail.

Fellow citizens, we'll meet violence with patient justice—assured of the rightness of our cause, and confident of the victories to come.

## Questions to Think About

1. What freedoms are presented in this excerpt?

2. According to Bush, what is the first responsibility of Americans in the fight for American principles?

3. **Draw a Conclusion** On which of FDR's four freedoms do the freedoms presented in Bush's speech appear to be based?

4. **Activity** Take one of the freedoms presented in President George W. Bush's Address to a Joint Session of Congress and describe how it is or is not exercised in the United States today. Write your response on a separate sheet of paper.

**THE COMING OF WAR**

# Reading a Chart

To support the United States war effort, peacetime industries had to be converted to war industries. The War Production Board directed this conversion, and many other government agencies helped coordinate subsequent production efforts. Productivity increased dramatically after the United States declared war. Bar charts can provide an effective way of summarizing changes in this productivity. ◆ *Read the text in Section 3 under the subheading "Mobilizing Industry." Then, examine the bar chart below and answer the questions on a separate sheet of paper.*

## Industry During World War II

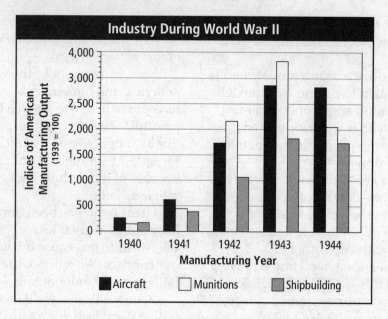

1. According to your text, what government agency oversaw wartime production?

2. According to the bar chart, which industry showed the most dramatic increase in production between 1940 and 1943?

3. Which industry showed the least dramatic increase in production between 1940 and 1943?

4. **Recognizing Cause and Effect** How would you explain the slight decline in the production of aircraft, munitions, and shipbuilding between 1943 and 1944?

5. **Draw Conclusions** How do you think increased manufacturing productivity affected the economy of the United States?

**THE COMING OF WAR**

# Section 1 Quiz

## A. Key Terms and People

**Directions:** *Choose the letter of the term or person that best fits each description. You will not use all the answers.*

**Column I**

_____ 1. theory of government in which a single party or leader maintains strict control

_____ 2. Russian leader who was known as the Great Terror

_____ 3. Italian leader who founded the Fascist Party

_____ 4. German dictator who wanted to unify all Germanic people into one state

_____ 5. prejudiced against Jewish people

_____ 6. policy of granting concessions

**Column II**

a. antisemitic

b. Adolf Hitler

c. appeasement

d. Benito Mussolini

e. Joseph Stalin

f. totalitarianism

g. Spanish Civil War

## B. Key Concepts

**Directions:** *Write the letter of the best answer or ending in each blank.*

_____ 7. After World War I, both Italy and Japan expected more
  a. financial assistance from the United States and Britain.
  b. guidance in establishing their own democratic governments.
  c. territory in exchange for their sacrifices during World War I.
  d. representation in the League of Nations.

_____ 8. Which political party rose to power in Germany during the 1930s?
  a. the Communist Party
  b. the Nazi Party
  c. the Fascist Party
  d. the Socialist Party

_____ 9. One of the ways that Mussolini maintained his power in Italy was by
  a. allowing freedom of the press.
  b. disbanding youth groups.
  c. supporting strikes.
  d. outlawing political parties.

_____ 10. The League of Nations did not prevent German and Italian aggression against other nations because it
  a. had no standing army and no real power to enforce its decrees.
  b. supported German and Italian aggression.
  c. focused only on Japanese aggression.
  d. was already involved in the Spanish Civil War.

## THE COMING OF WAR
# Section 2 Quiz

## A. Key Terms

**Directions:** *Choose the term that best completes each sentence. You will not use all the answers.*

**Column I**

_____ 1. included Britain, France, and eventually many other nations

_____ 2. included a cash-and-carry provision that aided the Allies

_____ 3. ensured that Germany, Italy, and Japan would fight on the same side

_____ 4. allowed President Roosevelt to provide any type of economic aid to the Allies

_____ 5. used their militaries to invade and control other nations

_____ 6. endorsed national self-determination

**Column II**

a. Allies

b. Atlantic Charter

c. Axis Powers

d. Lend-Lease Act

e. Tripartite Pact

f. Neutrality Act of 1939

g. blitzkrieg

## B. Key Concepts

**Directions:** *Write the letter of the best answer or ending in each blank.*

_____ 7. Roosevelt delivered his "Four Freedoms" speech to

  a. increase economic support for Britain.

  b. encourage Congress to support an immediate declaration of war.

  c. persuade Congress to take a neutral position in the war.

  d. appease Germany and other Axis Powers.

_____ 8. Interventionists believed that providing aid to Britain would

  a. draw the United States into war.

  b. keep the United States out of war.

  c. provoke attacks on the United States.

  d. prompt other countries to expect aid.

_____ 9. Who appeared to be winning the war in Europe at the end of 1940?

  a. Germany and Italy          c. Britain and France

  b. the Soviet Union           d. the United States

_____ 10. How did support for the Allies change following Roosevelt's reelection in 1940?

  a. Support decreased; Congress refused to provide additional aid.

  b. Support increased; Congress approved the Lend-Lease Act.

  c. Support increased; Congress urged the President to declare war.

  d. There was no change; the United States continued its isolationist policy.

**THE COMING OF WAR**
## Section 3 Quiz

### A. Key Terms and People

**Directions:** *Choose the letter of the term or person that best fits each description.*

**Column I**

_____ 1. U.S. navy base in the Pacific

_____ 2. a corps of women who provided support services to the U.S. Army

_____ 3. commander of the U.S. Army forces in Asia

_____ 4. long-distance relocation of American and Filipino prisoners by Japanese troops

_____ 5. battle that forced Japan to give up its quest for New Guinea

_____ 6. Japanese prime minister

**Column II**

a. Bataan Death March

b. Battle of Coral Sea

c. Douglas MacArthur

d. Pearl Harbor

e. Hideki Tojo

f. WAC

### B. Key Concepts

**Directions:** *Write the letter of the best answer or ending in each blank.*

_____ 7. The Japanese attacked Pearl Harbor because they wanted to
   a. gain control of the Hawaiian Islands.
   b. destroy ships and planes that threatened their expansion efforts.
   c. provoke the United States into declaring war.
   d. demonstrate their support for Germany and Italy.

_____ 8. Which ships survived the attack on Pearl Harbor untouched?
   a. battleships
   b. destroyers
   c. light cruisers
   d. aircraft carriers

_____ 9. After declaring war, the United States government
   a. repealed the Neutrality Act of 1939.
   b. enacted a draft because few Americans wanted to fight in the war.
   c. transformed peacetime industries into war industries.
   d. withdrew economic support from Britain.

_____ 10. After the United States declared war, the nation's economic situation
   a. improved.
   b. worsened.
   c. stalled.
   d. remained unchanged.

Name _____ Class _____ Date _____

## A. Key Terms and People

**Directions:** *Match the descriptions in Column I with the terms and people in Column II. Write the letter of the correct answer in the blank provided. (3 points each)*

**Column I**

_____ 1. theory of repressive government

_____ 2. dictator and head of the Nazi Party

_____ 3. document that endorsed national self-determination

_____ 4. "lightning war"

_____ 5. prime minister of Britain during World War II

_____ 6. Germany's peaceful union with Austria

_____ 7. signed by Germany, Italy, and Japan

_____ 8. the army auxiliary corps for women

_____ 9. general who staged a surprise attack on American forces

_____ 10. general who led the United States Army in Asia

**Column II**

a. Anschluss
b. Atlantic Charter
c. blitzkrieg
d. Winston Churchill
e. totalitarianism
f. Tripartite Pact
g. Adolf Hitler
h. Douglas MacArthur
i. Hideki Tojo
j. WAC

## B. Key Concepts

**Directions:** *Write the letter of the best answer or ending in each blank. (4 points each)*

_____ 11. Problems caused by the Great Depression made German people more likely to believe promises made by
a. the Weimar Republic.
b. Hitler's Nazi Party.
c. the United States.

_____ 12. To recover from the Great Depression, Japan
a. elected civilians to run the country.
b. spent less money on the military.
c. took control of resources in other nations.

_____ 13. The appeasement policy of the United States encouraged Germany to be
a. more aggressive.
b. less aggressive.
c. peaceful.

_____ 14. The Neutrality Act of 1939 allowed nations at war to buy supplies as long as they

    **a.** did not attack the United States.

    **b.** used the supplies for peaceful purposes only.

    **c.** paid cash and moved the supplies themselves.

_____ 15. Interventionists said that the United States could avoid war if it

    **a.** sent aid to Britain.       **c.** refused aid to all nations at war.

    **b.** refused aid to Britain.

_____ 16. Which of the following was seen as an economic declaration of war against the Axis Powers?

    **a.** the Tripartite Pact       **c.** the Lend-Lease Act

    **b.** the Atlantic Charter

_____ 17. Why did President Roosevelt place an embargo on important naval and aviation supplies in 1940?

    **a.** to make Japan declare war against the United States

    **b.** to stop Japan from expanding its empire

    **c.** to prevent war with Japan

_____ 18. What did the Office of War Mobilization do during the war?

    **a.** It monitored civilian activities.

    **b.** It supervised use of industry resources.

    **c.** It recruited soldiers for military service.

**Directions:** *Use this map of the Bataan Death March to answer questions 19 and 20.*

_____ 19. Where does the Bataan Peninsula lie in relation to Manila?

    **a.** east       **b.** west       **c.** north

_____ 20. About how many total miles did U.S. troops travel on the Bataan Death March?

    **a.** 65       **b.** 90       **c.** 125

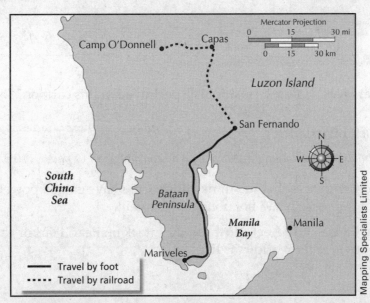

## C. Document-Based Assessment

**Directions:** *Use the political cartoon to answer this question on a separate sheet of paper.*
*(10 points)*

"*Look who's here again,*" Franklin D. Roosevelt Presidential Library

**21. Draw Inferences** How are isolationists portrayed in this cartoon? Explain.

## D. Critical Thinking

**Directions:** *Answer the following questions on a separate sheet of paper. (10 points each)*

**22. Predict Consequences** Do you think Hitler could have gained power in Germany
if the Great Depression had not occurred? Explain.

**23. Recognize Cause and Effect** How did the attack on Pearl Harbor cause the
United States to enter World War II?

**THE COMING OF WAR**

## Test B

## A. Key Terms and People

**Directions:** *Match the definitions in Column I with the terms and people in Column II. Write the correct letter in each blank. You will not use all the terms. (3 points each)*

**Column I**

_____ 1. theory of government in which one person or party controls all aspects of life

_____ 2. German dictator

_____ 3. document that strengthened the alliance between the United States and Britain

_____ 4. "lightning war"

_____ 5. British leader who said that Nazi aggression threatened all democracies

_____ 6. Germany's peaceful union with Austria

_____ 7. signed by the Axis Powers

_____ 8. army auxiliary corps for women

_____ 9. general who staged a surprise attack on Pearl Harbor

_____ 10. United States commander

**Column II**

a. Anschluss

b. appeasement

c. Joseph Stalin

d. Atlantic Charter

e. blitzkrieg

f. Winston Churchill

g. totalitarianism

h. Tripartite Pact

i. Adolf Hitler

j. Douglas MacArthur

k. Hideki Tojo

l. WAC

m. Neutrality Act of 1939

## B. Key Concepts

**Directions:** *Write the letter of the best answer or ending in each blank. (4 points each)*

_____ 11. How did the Great Depression eventually change Germany politically?

    a. Germans eventually believed that democracy would solve their problems.

    b. Germans eventually believed that Hitler would solve their problems.

    c. Thousands of Germans eventually emigrated to communist nations in search of jobs.

    d. The German parliament eventually became more powerful.

_____ 12. How did Japan attempt to recover from the Great Depression?

    a. Japan adopted democratic principles.

    b. Japan reduced military spending.

    c. Japan abandoned its constitutional monarchy.

    d. Japan seized control of resources in other nations.

_____ 13. What impact did the appeasement policy have on German aggression?

    a. It encouraged more aggression.

    b. It reduced aggression.

    c. It restricted aggression to certain regions.

    d. It brought peace to Europe.

_____ 14. The Neutrality Act of 1939 allowed nations at war to buy arms and other supplies from the United States as long as those nations
   a. agreed to keep the United States out of the conflict.
   b. promised not to use the materials against the United States.
   c. paid cash and transported the materials themselves.
   d. adopted democratic policies in their own countries.

_____ 15. Interventionists claimed that the United States could avoid war if it
   a. sent aid to Britain.
   b. refused aid to Britain.
   c. sent aid to all nations at war.
   d. refused aid to any nation at war.

_____ 16. Which of the following was perceived as being equivalent to declaring economic war against the Axis Powers?
   a. the Munich Pact
   b. the Tripartite Pact
   c. the Atlantic Charter
   d. the Lend-Lease Act

_____ 17. What goal did President Roosevelt hope to achieve when he enacting the embargo on naval and aviation supplies in 1940?
   a. to provoke Japan into war
   b. to stop Japanese expansion
   c. to avoid war with Japan
   d. to appease Japan

_____ 18. What role did the Office of War Mobilization play during the war?
   a. It issued propaganda statements.
   b. It monitored civilian activities.
   c. It supervised use of industry resources.
   d. It recruited soldiers for military service.

**Directions:** *Use this map of the Bataan Death March to answer questions 19 and 20.*

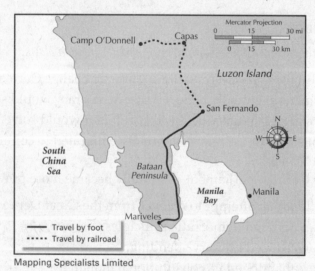

Mapping Specialists Limited

_____ 19. Where does the Bataan Peninsula lie in relation to Manila?
   a. east
   b. west
   c. north
   d. south

_____ **20.** About how many total miles did U.S. troops travel on the Bataan Death
March?

    **a.** 65                           **c.** 125

    **b.** 90                            **d.** 160

## C. Document-Based Assessment

**Directions:** *Use the political cartoon to answer this question on a separate sheet of paper.*
*(10 points)*

*"Look who's here again,"* Franklin D. Roosevelt Presidential Library

**21. Draw Inferences** How are isolationists portrayed in this cartoon? Explain.

## D. Critical Thinking

**Directions:** *Answer the following questions on the back of this paper or on a separate sheet of*
*paper. (10 points each)*

**22. Predict Consequences** Do you think a totalitarian form of government would
have formed in Germany if the Great Depression had not occurred? Explain.

**23. Identify Central Issues** What was the "Four Freedoms" speech, and why was it
significant?

# Answer Key

## Vocabulary Builder

Students' answers should demonstrate understanding of the vocabulary.

## Reading Strategy

1. Details that can be omitted include that *Stalin* means "man of steel" in Russian, and that he was known as the Great Terror.
2. Details that can be combined under a single concept include the mention of purging the Communist Party of real or suspected traitors and having most of the higher officers of the Red Army executed. These could all be combined under the concept "executions."
3. After Lenin's death in 1924, Joseph Stalin took Lenin's place as the head of the Communist Party. Stalin was a cruel and suspicious leader. His efforts to transform the Soviet Union into an industrial power and form state-run collective farms resulted in the deaths of millions, and Stalin had many people executed. This summary is about four lines long compared to the 11-line reading passage.

## Enrichment

Students' projects should demonstrate research, creative thinking, and appropriate presentation. Use *Assessment Rubrics* to evaluate the project.

## Outline Map
### German Aggression

Students should shade land that Germany claimed during 1935, 1936, and 1938.

1935— the Saar region, 1936— the Rhineland, 1938— Austria and the Sudentenland.

## Interpreting a Political Cartoon
### Neutrality

1. The man represents the U.S. Senate because he's holding a sign labeled "U.S. Senate."
2. The man is holding up his hand to symbolize the U.S. Senate's attempt to keep the world at arm's length.
3. The boats and airplanes represent American commercial interests, as suggested by the banner across from the man. The boats and planes cover the globe, suggesting that the United States is doing business with nations all over the world.
4. The cartoonist is saying that it is hypocritical of the United States to take a neutral stance on foreign military conflicts, because the United States is already involved in foreign affairs through its commercial enterprises.

## Primary Source
### The "Four Freedoms" Speech

freedom of speech and expression; freedom of every person to worship God in his own way; freedom from want; freedom from fear

to let Americans know that these freedoms were being threatened

Germany, Italy and Japan had invaded other countries. Germany was also threatening Britain.

The speech helped remind Americans that many people value freedom; the United States should help countries who fight for freedom; and Americans should probably prepare for war.

# Answer Key

## The "Four Freedoms" Speech and George W. Bush's Address to a Joint Session of Congress

1. freedom of religion, freedom of speech, freedom to vote and assemble and disagree with each other
2. The first responsibility of Americans is to live by these principles.
3. Sample answer: The freedoms presented in Bush's speech appear to be based on FDR's first two freedoms: freedom of speech and expression, and freedom of every person to worship God in his or her own way.
4. Student responses will vary. Sample answer: All citizens 18 years or older can exercise their right to vote by voting in local, state, and federal elections.

## Reading a Chart
## Industry During World War Two

1. Office of War Mobilization
2. munitions
3. shipbuilding
4. Possible answer: The slight decline may suggest that the military had the materials that were needed.
5. More people were needed to produce the products needed for war. This means jobs were created. People with jobs earned and spent money, which helped stimulate the economy. This increased manufacturing productivity helped end the Great Depression.

## Section 1 Quiz

1. f  2. e  3. d  4. b  5. a
6. c  7. c  8. b  9. d  10. a

## Section 2 Quiz

1. a  2. f  3. e  4. d  5. b
6. b  7. a  8. b  9. a  10. a

## Section 3 Quiz

1. d  2. f  3. c  4. a  5. b
6. e  7. b  8. d  9. c  10. a

## Test A

1. e  2. g  3. b  4. c  5. d
6. a  7. f  8. j  9. i  10. h
11. b  12. c  13. a  14. c  15. a
16. c  17. b  18. b  19. b  20. b
21. Sample answer: Isolationists are portrayed as being inconsistent in their beliefs. The two isolationists holding the long list of complaints about the Pearl Harbor attack suggest that when war came to American shores, isolationists believed that Roosevelt had not done enough to prepare for war.
22. Sample answer: No. If the Great Depression had not occurred, the Weimar Republic might have had time to solve the economic problems that followed World War I. With increased economic stability, Germans might have had no need to look to a dictator who promised them a return to greatness. Sample answer: Yes. Even if the Great Depression had not occurred, the German people would still have been unhappy. The defeat of Germany during World War I was a blow to its national esteem. One way to rebuild that esteem was to create a great nation of Germanic people, which Hitler promised to do.
23. Sample answer: The attack on Pearl Harbor caused the United States to enter World War II for several reasons. Firstly, there was little chance that such a dramatic attack could have gone without some sort of military response. Secondly, the attack unified American isolationists and interventionists. A united House of Representatives voted 388 to 1 to declare war, and the Senate joined them unanimously.

# Answer Key

## Test B

1. g    2. i    3. d    4. e    5. f
6. a    7. h    8. l    9. k    10. j
11. b   12. d   13. a   14. c   15. a
16. d   17. b   18. c   19. b   20. b

21. Sample answer: Isolationists are portrayed as being inconsistent in their beliefs. In the cartoon, a banner flying over the hillside camp suggests that isolationists believe that Roosevelt's preparations for war will cause war. Yet, the two isolationists holding the long list of complaints about the Pearl Harbor attack suggest that when war came to American shores, isolationists believed that Roosevelt hadn't done enough to prepare for war.

22. Students may take different approaches to this question. One approach is to say no. If the Great Depression had not occurred, the Weimar Republic might have had time to solve the economic problems that followed World War I. With increased economic stability, Germans might have had no need to look to a totalitarian leader who promised them a return to greatness. Another approach is to say yes. Even if the Great Depression had not occurred, the German people would still be unhappy. The defeat of Germany during World War I was a blow to its national esteem. One way to rebuild that esteem was to create a great nation of Germanic people, which Hitler promised to do.

23. The "Four Freedoms" speech was the name given to Roosevelt's State of the Union address in 1941. It followed the fall of France, the blitz of London, and the Tripartite Pact negotiated among Germany, Italy and Japan. In the speech, Roosevelt stressed four important freedoms: freedom of speech, freedom of religion, freedom from want, and freedom from fear. He said that the United States should support other nations that strive to maintain those freedoms in the face of oppression. The speech foreshadowed the Lend-Lease Act, the Atlantic Charter, and ultimately Roosevelt's decision to go to war.